HISTORY DIVISION (BIOGRAPHY SECTION)

General Editor: G. M. D. HOWAT

A Prophet in Two Countries

THE LIFE OF F. E. SIMON

F. E. SIMON, 1954

(*Photograph by courtesy of Lotte Meitner-Graf*)

A Prophet
in Two Countries

THE LIFE OF F. E. SIMON

by

NANCY ARMS

PERGAMON PRESS

OXFORD · LONDON · EDINBURGH · NEW YORK
TORONTO · PARIS · FRANKFURT

Pergamon Press Ltd., Headington Hill Hall, Oxford
4 & 5 Fitzroy Square, London W.1

Pergamon Press (Scotland) Ltd., 2 & 3 Teviot Place, Edinburgh 1

Pergamon Press Inc., 44-01 21st Street, Long Island City, New York 11101

Pergamon of Canada Ltd., 6 Adelaide Street East, Toronto, Ontario

Pergamon Press S.A.R.L., 24 rue des Ecoles, Paris 5e

Pergamon Press GmbH, Kaiserstrasse 75, Frankfurt-am-Main

*Made and printed in Great Britain by C. Tinling and Co., Ltd.,
Liverpool, London and Prescot*

(2537/66)

Contents

Acknowledgements

It is sad that during the writing of this book two of the people most closely connected with it have died – Mrs. Frank, Sir Francis's elder sister, and Dr. Paul Rosbaud. To Mrs. Frank I am indebted for all the information about the Simon home in Berlin. Without Dr. Rosbaud's encouragement and sensitive understanding of people and events the biography would have been abandoned within the first six months.

Lady Simon and her daughters have been unsparing in their readiness to help me. Lady Simon has put at my disposal all her husband's papers. At considerable cost to herself in the memories they have revived she has sorted through quantities of correspondence for my benefit. She has introduced me to many people whose connections with Sir Francis have been helpful to my researches. Above all she has brought to life for me a period and a country I did not know. If only for the excuse it has given me to visit her so often, this book has been a pleasure to write.

Dr. Kurti is an old friend and has had this friendship severely tested in the demands I have made on his time and patience. Without his guidance and correction it would have been impossible for me to write about low temperature physics. On a wider field he has been constantly helpful in suggestions and introductions.

Professor Peierls is another friend on whose assistance I knew I could rely. I am most grateful to him for talking to me about the war years and for reading these chapters.

I am greatly indebted to the following for their help and, often, their hospitality: Miss Esther Simpson, Dr. Clara von Simson, Professor G. O. Jones, Mr. M. W. Perrin, Dr. A. Cooke, Dr. K. Mendelssohn, Dr. J. Wilks.

I should like to thank Professor E. N. da C. Andrade for kindly answering a query about refugee problems, Dr. H. Mendelssohn for information conveyed in a letter to Dr. Kurti, and Professor J. Lesley for the memories of Aldeburgh and Berlin which he sent to Lady Simon.

I am grateful to the following for their kind permission to quote excerpts: *Nature* (1936, 1937, 1939, 1949), *Research* (1952), *Harlequin* (1950), The *Financial Times* (1948, 1951, 1952, 1955), The *Sunday Times* (1937, 1956), and Messrs. Basil Blackwell & Mott Ltd. for excerpts from *The Neglect of Science* (1951).

The following have generously allowed their photographs to be reproduced: Lotte Meitner-Graf (frontispiece), Kay Simmon (1953), Oxford Photocrafts (1945) and the *Oxford Mail* (1952).

CHAPTER 1

A Jewish Home in Berlin

Two wars and their aftermath have altered beyond recognition the Berlin in which Franz Simon was born on July 2nd, 1893; a savage régime obliterated the Jewish community in which he grew up. Yet no suspicion that it was to play so hideous a part in modern history ruffled either the city or the community in the early years of the twentieth century. Berlin was at the height of its prosperity. Compared with London, Paris, Vienna and other great European capitals, it was new, for, until the Franco-Prussian War and the treaty that ended it in 1871, Berlin had been no more than a provincial capital. Now it was a rapidly growing metropolis, the administrative head of a mighty empire, the financial centre of a country that in its technical achievements was swiftly outstripping the rest of the world, and the magnet attracting all that was new in science, industry and the arts. Throughout Germany the speed and success of its enterprises engendered a spirit of confidence and adventure, and people crowded to Berlin to find work in its fine, modern factories and to make their fortunes in the city that was the hub of this exciting new era.

A boom in the building trade was the natural outcome of this influx into the city, and a large part of the Berlin that survived until the Second World War was built during this period: solid, pretentious houses for the wealthy in the vicinity of the Tiergarten; streets of mean tenements for the workers in the city's East End; schools, hospitals, theatres and museums, everywhere and for all. As the price of land soared, so did the incomes of those who traded in it, particularly when, like Franz Simon's father, they had the imagination to envisage future developments.

I

A*

One of the twelve children of a Silesian hardware merchant, Ernst Simon had grown up in a family where money was scarce. Franz liked to tell the story he had heard of the somewhat haphazard financial arrangements of his grandfather's family, how each of its members paid his earnings into a common receptacle and each, in an equally uncharted manner, helped himself. Certainly Ernst's share of the family funds was negligible, nor was his education in any way worthy of his ability. When he left home he held a variety of small jobs which enabled him over the course of years to save enough money to buy his first piece of land. This he sold at considerable profit. Gradually, as his transactions became increasingly successful, he acquired enough capital to set up in business on his own. His interest lay in developing the land he bought, and in doing this he was able to use his gifts of imagination and perspicacity to sense the way in which certain pieces of land could be most suitably and profitably used. By the time that his children were born he had won for himself a respected position as one of Berlin's most successful dealers in land.

Unlike so many who have made their way from comparative poverty to considerable wealth, Ernst Simon was no ruthless, hard-headed business man. It is true that he managed his money in a less perfunctory manner than his Silesian forebears, but for him money meant responsibility, not only for his immediate family but for his numerous brothers and sisters. One of his brothers, who later became a well-known judge, considered that he owed a large part of his success to Ernst's generosity; another, after the death of Ernst's first partner, his wife's uncle, became a partner in his business. Because he felt the inadequacy of his own education, he was anxious for his children to enjoy the advantages he had missed, and delighted in spending money on travel, concerts, theatres, pictures and books. He was intensely interested in every detail of his son's education and sent his two daughters to universities at a time when higher education for women was not as common as it is today. It has been suggested by those who knew him that Ernst's personal qualities, his integrity and reliability, had helped to make his profession one which was respected in Berlin. Like Galsworthy's Timothy Forsyte, Ernst Simon dealt

only in gilt-edged securities, not like Timothy from nervous-
ness, but because his strict code of honour made him regard
playing the stockmarket in the same dubious light as gambling.
He was a kindly, sensitive man, often over-anxious about his
children and fearful that they might be spoiled by too much
money.

Franz's mother, who had been born Anna Mendelssohn, was
also of Silesian stock. Her father, Philibert Mendelssohn, was
a mathematician, with the title of "koeniglich preussischer
Rechnungsrat", in the Prussian geodetic service. This was an
unusual position for a Jew since Jews rarely became civil
servants or had anything to do with scientific matters. None
of his three sons followed his scientific bent, but his three
grandsons all made names for themselves as scientists: Franz
Simon, the low temperature physicist; Heinrich Mendelssohn,
who became a zoologist and settled in Israel; Kurt Mendelssohn, who, like Franz, became a low temperature physicist
and emigrated to England, and who still works at the Claren-
don Laboratory in Oxford. To a certain extent Franz, as the
eldest of the cousins, was to blaze a trail for the others in a
family where science was considered "not fit for Jews" and
as "brotlose Kunst" (an unprofitable occupation). When Heinrich was trying to persude his father to let him study zoology,
he was abetted by an uncle who remembered that Franz
Simon had also insisted on having his own way about his
career and was not doing too badly at science; at least he was
making a living.

Anna Simon was an elegant, good-looking woman with a
particularly attractive voice, keenly interested in painting and
music, and with an extensive knowledge of both. For years
she took painting lessons and throughout her life devoted most
of her spare time to painting, either on holiday or in the parks
of Berlin. Still life was her speciality. A friend once remarked
that it was almost impossible to finish one's breakfast in peace
at the Simons, so anxious was Anna to rearrange the table
for her next study. As her two daughters — Mimi, the eldest
of the family, and Ebeth, the youngest — grew up, she shared
her enthusiasms with them, introducing them to the picture
galleries and museums of Berlin, taking them on pilgrimages

to the art treasures of Munich, Florence and Rome, and enjoying with them the excellent music so readily available in their own city. Her husband and son kept aloof from this artistic world, and it was not until Franz married that he showed even the slightest interest in the pursuits that were so important to his mother and sisters. That he inherited some of his mother's talent was shown in his lifelong hobby, photography, for coupled with his competence, technically and in composition, was his skill in choosing a subject, so that many of his character studies and landscapes are works of art.

Ernst Simon's increasing prosperity made it possible for him and his partner to buy in 1904 a house and ten acres of parkland in Wilmersdorf, a western suburb of Berlin, which in those days was on the edge of the country, but which soon became caught in the tentacles of the rapidly spreading town. The Simons for a few years regarded this as their summer residence, for they and their uncle's family occupied it alternate summers until 1909 when it was sold, most profitably, to the city authorities who intended to build a large town hall there and develop it as a civic centre. But their plans took so long to materialize that war came to put an end to building projects, so that it became instead a public park, the Preussen Park, and exists as such today.

Perhaps because they moved there in the impressionable period between childhood and adulthood, perhaps because, looking back, they saw it as a sanctuary from an increasingly difficult world, the house that the Simon family remembered as home was the house in the Landhausstrasse where they moved in 1909 from a flat near the Tiergarten. Externally, in its somewhat ugly solidity, with its three storeys and large garden, it bore a strong resemblance to many English houses built in the same period and still to be seen in the prosperous suburbs of our big cities, but the interior owed much to the artistic taste of Franz's mother, who delighted in furnishing and arranging the large, well-proportioned rooms. Franz himself took many photographs to show the fine ceilings and panellings, the paintings, the magnificent chandeliers and the substantial furniture, which, though too heavy for modern taste, is still remarkable for the beauty of its wood and the perfection of its craftsmanship. One of the carpets, some of the paintings (including Anna's own work) and furniture, among the latter a set of handsome dining room chairs and a massive mahogany bookcase, were, until Mimi's death in 1962, still in use in her flat in London, and bring to life the photographs in Franz's album. These include some taken for a journal by a professional photographer, for, even in that wealthy area of Berlin, Landhausstrasse 14/15 was a house of exceptional quality.

The style in which the Simons lived, their interest in the arts and education, were not unusual in the community to which they belonged, but their community was unique in the capitals of Europe. In no other city was the Jewish population so large, so wealthy or so influential. Wherever they have lived the Jews have always valued intellectual achievements, but never before had historical events combined to bring so many of them together in one place with sufficient money to indulge their tastes. For a brief period of time they made their phenomenal contribution to the cultural, industrial and financial life of Germany, sunned themselves in the prosperity they had helped to create, and were then ruthlessly eradicated.

Germany had been slow in giving even a nominal freedom to the Jews, and in the early years of the twentieth century certain professions were still barred to them; they could not become, for instance, higher civil servants, officers in the army or full university professors. Some evaded these prohibitions by Christian baptism, a few were so outstanding that they were accepted in spite of their religion, but the majority concentrated on the careers that had always been open to them, and these were largely in the world of law, medicine and finance. From the days of the great persecutions of the Middle Ages their experience had proved that money was the key to freedom and safety, and the clannishness of the Jewish family, however scattered it might be, gave them widespread connections which became more and more valuable as the money-lender became the banker and in the course of time was called upon to finance Germany's industrial boom. The speed with which Germany gained industrial supremacy was due in the first place to the skill of its technicians and the support they received from a far-sighted government, in the second to the financial ability of the Jews in keeping the country economically sound. They settled in Berlin, the financial as well as the geographical capital, to make money and to spend it, some constructively by collecting pictures, financing art galleries, theatres and museums, running liberal newspapers, encouraging artists, writers and musicians; others squandered it worthlessly and ostentatiously, incurring for their race the dislike and contempt which Hitler was to fan into hatred and persecution. So interdependent were Jewish and German interests that the Jews in Germany were more anxious than in most countries to identify themselves, at least publicly, with the customs and ideas of the country to which they belonged, with the result that foreigners often believed the Jews to be more deeply assimilated in Germany than elsewhere. Many became intensely patriotic German subjects, proud of the brilliant new empire that Bismarck had built and anxious to fulfil their obligations as Germans. Aby Warburg, founder of the Warburg Institute, had identified himself so completely with Germany and was so grateful for the Kaiser's kindness to the Jews that he welcomed his military service with enthusiasm, even though later, when in 1914 Germany ignored Belgian neutrality, he was to be disgusted and disillusioned. Franz's father, though ill at the time of a plebiscite in Silesia, felt it his duty as a good German to make the journey there to register his vote, even at great personal inconvenience.

The Simons were not practising Jews, though Frau Simon occasionally attended the synagogue on high feast days. Herr Simon actively disliked religious observances; he believed that his mother's insistence on meticulously obeying Jewish festival rites when she was in poor health had been responsible for her death. The Simons had as many non-Jewish as Jewish friends. Their interests were cultural, their politics liberal, and, though aware and ashamed of the parvenu behaviour of a minority of their community, they were not seriously disturbed by the anti-Semitism which was making insidious progress in Germany. Certainly young Franz was to be unconscious of it for many years to come.

Those who knew Franz in his boyhood remember him as a

shy, quiet, self-contained boy, showing no signs of the talents for which his father watched so eagerly. As he looked around at Germany's industrial achievements, Herr Simon dreamed of a technical career for his son and showered him with expensive toys in the hope of kindling his interest. Franz enjoyed them, but not more than any other boy, and refused to be hurried, making his leisurely, unspectacular way through the early years of reading, writing and arithmetic in the Vorschule of the Kaiser Wilhelm Reform Gymnasium. German children start school at the age of six, but, since Franz's birthday was in July and the school year started in April, he was nearly seven when he entered the Vorschule, the equivalent of an English primary school. Unwilling for Franz to fall behind because of the unfortunate timing of his birth, his father had provided him with extra lessons so that Franz was able to enter the second year class and so remain almost a year younger than most of his fellows until a setback later in his school career brought him back on an age level with those with whom he should have started. After the Vorschule the German child moved on to the Gymnasium proper, where a choice had to be made between two types of education, that provided by the Humanistische Gymnasium, where the emphasis was on the Classics, and the Real Gymnasium where science occupied three quarters of the curriculum. The latter would have been Herr Simon's choice for Franz, but he was persuaded against it by his wife's family who favoured the more liberal type of education of the Humanistische Gymnasium. Their decision initiated the unhappiest years of Franz's life.

Throughout Germany at that time the calibre of the teachers, with a few notable exceptions, was poor. Their pay and social position bore no relation to their responsibilities, while so great were the opportunities offered by industry and so inflexible and devoid of vision was the whole educational system that only the less able graduates were attracted to the profession. Einstein once said that the teachers in the primary schools seemed to him like sergeants, those in the Gymnasium like lieutenants; certainly there were similarities between the school and the barracks. Obedience and discipline were the most prized virtues; pupils did not speak unless they were spoken to, they stood to attention when addressed, and the greater part of their learning was in the form of mechanical repetition. Franz's lifelong distaste for memorizing dull facts—and as such he regarded Latin and Greek grammar — and the unimaginative way in which they were presented led to such an open hatred of the Classics and of those who taught them that he brought upon his head retributive measures that amounted almost to persecution. Bored and frustrated, he isolated himself from pupils and teachers alike, and gained a reputation for haughtiness and eccentricity, neither of which qualities is calculated to win popularity at school. Mathematics and physics were the only subjects in which he took any interest, and even in mathematics he showed a stubborn and tactless inclination to argue with the teacher, who insisted that the correct answers, as supplied by Franz, were not enough and that the stages by which they were reached were a necessary part of a mathematical exercise.

Fortunately Franz kept his school reports, an unhappy record of diminishing interest. At the Vorschule, apart from singing, all the subjects were good or very good, but his first term at the Gymnasium earned the comments: "He could do better ... He must become more serious and attentive if he wishes to be moved up into the next form." His "industry" and "attention" were unsatisfactory and most subjects were only "genuegend" (fair). As he moved up the school, physics, mathematics and English remained "gut" or "sehr gut", his writing continued — and persisted — bad, and the main subjects of the curriculum, Latin, Greek and French, never rose above "mangelhaft" (unsatisfactory). The result was that the teachers of these subjects, inevitably losing patience with him, at last insisted that he stayed down in one form for another year. This was a disgrace so serious that, nowadays, coming at that particular stage of his schooling, it would have prevented him from entering a university. Several of the teachers felt that it was undeserved and one of them told Franz's father that at the meeting where the decision was taken the headmaster had remarked that it was a permanent reflection on the school to keep down a boy of the calibre of Franz Simon.

Franz never forgot the misery of his schooldays, and his lack

of success influenced his later attitude to education. He grew
to feel more kindly disposed to Latin and Greek, regarding
them as valuable components of the broad type of education
he advocated, but insistence on success at school remained
abhorrent to him and he was quite perturbed when his
daughters' early reports were good. His own failures made him
sympathetic towards those whose academic record was poor
or who developed late, and encouraged him to give them a
chance which others might have refused. He deplored specializ-
ing too young, especially since this normally meant the
accumulation of facts without the stimulus to think. He main-
tained that he would never have gained an entrance to an
English university since his memory for facts was so poor.

The year that Franz was kept down was always remembered
by the Simon family for the effect it had on their father. He
had followed with acute anxiety his son's unsatisfactory progress, providing extra lessons in the hope of changing its course,
fitting up a private laboratory for him at the first dawn of an
interest in physics, distressed out of all proportion by the bad
reports that Franz would often conceal under the carpet to
postpone the hour of revelation. When he heard that Franz
had been kept down, he was shattered; he behaved almost as
though he had lost a son. More than half a century later Mimi,
Franz's elder sister, could recall her father's stricken face when
he appeared, just after he had heard the news, at a party she
was having with her friends.

His father's anxieties made it impossible for Franz to forget
the miseries of school life even at home, though the affection
of his family and his growing interest in science did much to
alleviate them. As his younger sister, Ebeth, grew up, his
amused enjoyment of the little girl he had loved to tease
developed into a lasting friendship so that, until he married,
she was closer to him than anyone else. He was not socially
inclined and had few friends, the greatest of whom was Lutz
Heck, who later became a zoologist and director of the Berlin
zoo; much of Franz's spare time was spent in helping him with
his experiments. Gradually science began to engross him.
Even as a boy he disliked the imprecise, unscientific descrip-
tion of natural phenomena. His aunt, carrying her son, Kurt

Mendelssohn, hanging limply over her arm, begged the child not to make himself so heavy. "He can't make himself heavier than he is," said Franz. However irritating the remark might have been to his aunt, it reflected the importance he attached to accuracy even in so minor a matter. His mother worried because his reading was so limited and searched for books she considered suitable – history, literature, art – leaving them about where he was bound to find them. One day to her delight she noticed Franz sitting in an apple tree, engrossed in a book. When she discovered the title she realized her rejoicings were premature; it was a book on mathematics. It seems likely that Franz's reading habits would not have differed greatly even if he had had more imaginative guidance at school or less anxious expectancy at home. He was never a novel reader and might well have by-passed that stage in so many people's development when they will read any book, good or bad, as long as it tells a story. He never read what other people thought he should read, only what interested him, and as a schoolboy this was very little. As his interest in people grew and the world of politics and international affairs forced themselves upon his cognizance, so the character of his library developed to include, alongside the scientific literature, books of biography, history, political philosophy, humour and satire.

Fortunately for Franz, Herr Simon's preoccupation with his son's education found more pleasurable outlets than post-mortems on school reports. He believed in the value of holidays and of travel, and, even before they took their children with them, he and his wife had travelled more than was customary in most families, particularly at that time. Frau Simon was a bad sailor and, after an exceptionally rough voyage to Egypt in 1904 when she had begged her husband to set up in business there rather than subject her to the return journey, she tried in general to restrict her travelling to countries that could be reached by land. But they visited London for the coronation of Edward VII, staying at the Hotel Cecil, where Shell Mex House now stands, and in 1907 Herr Simon took Franz and Mimi to see the sights of London and thence to the Isle of Wight and the Channel Islands. Through some German friends they had been put in touch with a Scottish tweed manufacturer

and his family, the Browns of Galashiels, and, when the
Simons returned to Germany, Gracie Brown, who was Mimi's
age, came to stay with them for a year. From her they all
learned the rudiments of spoken English, with the exception
of Herr Simon who never advanced beyond, "Cheese, please!".
Franz and Mimi made several journeys to England to improve
their English and to acquire some knowledge of English life
and customs, Mimi going farther afield to Galashiels while
Franz stayed with families in Ilfracombe, Folkestone and Aldeburgh. He became as friendly with the Lesleys in Aldeburgh
as Mimi was with the Browns of Galashiels. The Lesleys had
two sons, Norman, who was Franz's age and was drowned
in a submarine in 1917, and Jimmy, the elder, at that time an
undergraduate at Cambridge. Through him Franz made his
first acquaintance with the buildings and educational system
of the two great English universities for which he was later
to have so much respect and affection. Franz made a strong
impression on the Lesleys. They found him far more intelligent
than the majority of English boys of his age, and were amazed
at the energy with which he flung himself into all the sports
their sons enjoyed. In 1913 Jimmy Lesley paid a return visit to
Berlin where he was shown the sights, taken to theatres and
concerts, entertained at family parties, and introduced to the
German card game "Skat", for which Frau Simon had a special
fondness. In 1917 when he was a prisoner of war near Coburg
the Simons wrote offering to send him food, at a time when
they and all German civilians were severely rationed. He and
Franz never lost touch with each other. They met for the last
time, both of them professors then, in Oxford in 1950 at the
wedding of Franz's younger daughter.

Whatever the time of the year the Simons took the appro-
priate holiday, often going overseas in the summer and spending the winter holidays nearer home at winter sports in the
Tyrol or the Engadine or attending a ski-course at Zell-am-
See. Franz's favourite sports were tennis, riding and ski-ing, the
first abandoned after the war because of an elbow injury, the
last two when he could no longer afford them. The year
that Franz was kept down the family went to Lake Geneva,
but he was not allowed to stay with them at Montreux, being

sent instead to improve his French at a school in Vevey. The severity of this punishment was considerably mitigated by the presence at the school of a number of English boys with whom Franz quickly made friends, so that his English continued to improve at the expense of his French, a circumstance not anticipated by his father when he chose a Swiss school.

In the summer of 1913, Herr Simon, Mimi and Franz, little knowing that this was to be their last foreign holiday together, made their most extensive tour, visiting Holland and Belgium, and cruising via Southampton, Lisbon and Gibraltar through the Mediterranean to Genoa where they met Frau Simon who had travelled overland. The family were to go on to Naples, but Franz had to report at Augsburg for military service. On the station at Genoa he bade them a disconsolate farewell, depressed at the curtailment of his holiday and at the prospect of uncongenial employment. Within the year war was declared, changing the face of the Germany of his youth, closing the frontiers of countries he was growing to know and understand, and separating him, in some cases for ever, from the friends he was learning to make and the work he now enjoyed.

CHAPTER 2

University Life — and War

THE war put an end for the time being to the scientific course
on which, now that his unsatisfactory schooldays were over,
Franz was happily and successfully launched. He took his
"Abiturium", the school leaving certificate and necessary quali-
fication for university entrance, at Easter, 1912, when he was
eighteen. His father still hoped that he would take the training
necessary for a technological career, but it had become increasingly obvious to Franz during his last years in school that he
was interested in physics and mathematics not as tools to be
used for immediate, practical purposes but for their intrinsic
value as subjects for study and research. Although Herr Simon
was impressed by the contribution science was making to industry, his main reason for wishing Franz to take up the
industrial as opposed to the academic side of science was that
he regarded pure science as a luxury occupation, and he had a
horror of the rich man's son who, because he was financially
secure, wasted his time in dilettante pursuits. Fortunately, Franz
found an ally in a family friend, Professor Leonor Michaelis,
a biologist at one of the Berlin hospitals and later at the Rocke-
feller Institute, New York. He had invited Franz during his
last two years at school to spend part of his holidays working
in his laboratory and had been impressed by his keenness.
Naturally the Simons turned to Professor Michaelis for advice
about Franz's future, and it was he who finally persuaded
Herr Simon that Franz would be wasting his talents if he were
forced into industry.

Undoubtedly, the account that Michaelis was able to give
of the state of science at that time was instrumental in in-
fluencing Herr Simon's decision. Twenty years before, in the

latter part of the nineteenth century, physics, chemistry and mathematics, as well as many non-scientific subjects, were intellectually in the doldrums. The basic principles enunciated by such men as Newton, Kelvin, Helmholtz and Maxwell had been in general understood and digested and a great many of their practical consequences worked out, so that some, at least, of the public figures in the world of science had openly asserted their belief that no great new discoveries would be made, and that physics, in particular, would be confined to the detailed elucidation of known principles and the more accurate measurement of an increasing number of quantities. A change in this situation coincided almost exactly with the turn of the century. In 1900, Max Planck produced a theory about the emission of light which, though it did not appear particularly startling at the time, was to lead to the quantum theory. In 1905, Einstein first propounded his theory of relativity as applicable to light and motion, thus clarifying fields in which physicists had found Newtonian mechanics least satisfying. In Berlin the young chemist, Walther Nernst, was evolving the Third Law of Thermodynamics; in Göttingen Klein, the mathematician, was enlarging the scope of mathematics to include new and exciting research in physics and astronomy. The work of scientists outside Germany — Niels Bohr's theory of the atom, the discoveries of Rutherford and the Curies in the field of radioactivity — had stimulated enormous activity among German scientists. New discoveries revealed new opportunities and by 1912 the whole world of science was in ferment; German scientists began to surge ahead, winning prestige for their country in all branches of physics, mathematics, chemistry and medicine. Nor were their names known only in universities and laboratories. However little the man in the street might understand of Einstein's theory of relativity, the press saw to it that he shared in the storm of controversy it aroused among the philosophers of Europe. Newspapers carried headlines reporting the latest developments in physics and allied subjects as presented to the impressive gathering of international scientists — among them Nernst, Planck, Rutherford, Mme. Curie, Poincaré, Langevin and Einstein — who attended the Solvay Conference in Brussels in 1911.

Closely connected with the running of this conference were two men who were to play important parts in Simon's life : Nernst was responsible for selecting the representatives from various countries, and F. A. Lindemann (later Lord Cherwell) was the secretary.

Professor Michaelis won his case for physics and Franz matriculated at the University of Munich in the spring of 1912, immediately after his "Abiturium". In Germany no examination, like the English B.A. or B.Sc., separates undergraduate studies from research work for a doctor's degree. Often the student in the days before the first war would spend two or three years enjoying a somewhat haphazard curriculum at different universities before settling down at one for the last two or possibly three years before his final degree. The only record considered necessary by the authorities was that provided by the booklet, variously called a "Kollegienbuch", "Anmeldungbuch", "Anmeldebuch", in which he wrote down the lectures he had chosen to attend. Even this was largely a formality since no register of attendance was kept, no examinations were taken, and the lecturer who signed the booklet frequently knew no more of his student, unless they met for practical work, than that he had paid his fees.

Simon attended the Ludwig Maximilian University, Munich, from April 24th, 1912, until March 30th, 1913, and spent the summer term of 1913 at the Georg August University, Göttingen. It was customary for the student to consider the first two terms of his university career as an opportunity for taking work rather light-heartedly. Simon followed this precedent in his first term at Munich, though he undertook a heavy timetable in his second. The subjects studied in his first term were experimental and theoretical physics, differential calculus and thermodynamics; in the second term he increased the time spent on these and added to them inorganic chemistry and microscopic techniques, as well as some extra classes in practical physics at the Technische Hochschule. He was unlikely to have been so far advanced in physics and mathematics as a student from a Real Gymnasium and must have worked exceedingly hard to have received such consistently good reports. "Sehr gut" was the highest commendation obtainable and this he earned for his "Fleiss" (industry), "Aufmerksamkeit" (attentiveness) and "Fortgang" (progress) in both these subjects. Since the "Kollegienbuch" records also the fees paid for the lectures it provides an interesting source of comparison not only between the costs of different German universities, but with other European universities at the same period. The average fee at Munich was about M.20 a term for each subject at a time when the mark was worth roughly a shilling.

German university years are divided into two terms or semesters, the summer term lasting from Easter until early August, the winter from October to February. After his two terms at Munich Simon transferred to Göttingen, the centre of mathematical research in Germany; it is difficult to imagine two university towns more different in character. Munich was the most important town, politically and intellectually, of southern Germany. Largely Roman Catholic, it was in many ways more democratic, less class-conscious than Berlin, and Simon with his liberal background appreciated its open dislike of Prussia and militarism. As a centre of artistic life it tried, not always successfully, to vie with Paris, housing in its Latin Quarter, Schwabing, a thriving community of painters. Its university attracted professors of the highest calibre, students packed its friendly cafés and biergartens, its museums and concert halls drew visitors from all over the world, and the beautiful lakes and mountains within easy reach of the city provided every variety of winter and summer sport. At Munich Simon tasted for the first time the freedom of being grown up and the pleasures to be shared with companions of his own age and intellectual tastes. We know from the photographs he took how much he enjoyed the beauty of the town and its surroundings, as well as the social activities they provided. One of his finest photographic character studies is of the proprietress of one of Munich's most famous cabarets, a favourite rendezvous for university students. For the first time in his life he was beginning to take an interest in the opposite sex, and worried his father by spending too much money on expensive suits. Perhaps Herr Simon was relieved when Franz moved to Göttingen where social life was on a different plane.

Whereas Munich was gay and up-to-date, Göttingen was

peaceful and old-fashioned. Its charm lay in its old walls and medieval architecture, its importance in its university. Like Oxford and Cambridge before industry moved in, Göttingen was primarily a university town, in which the shopkeepers and boarding house proprietors were as dependent, indirectly, on the university for their livelihood as were the teachers and administrators directly supported by it. Gauss, the great nineteenth-century mathematician, had been responsible for establishing the international prestige of the Georg August University of Göttingen. He had been followed by another famous mathematician, Klein, who, in his desire to further the practical applications of his subject, had initiated the work which was to encourage wealthy industrialists, more aware than those of other countries of the importance of science to national efficiency, to endow the numerous technical institutes that provided within the walls of the sleepy old city some of the most modern techniques and equipment in the world. Drawn by the fame of the university and its teachers came other mathematicians, Minkowski and, greatest of them all, Hilbert, followed later by the physicists, James Franck and Max Born, the latter taking his degree there in 1917 and returning as a professor after the war. Here in Göttingen were held annually the Darmstadt lectures, given by the most distinguished scientists of the age, among them Niels Bohr, Planck, Nernst, Sommerfeld, Lorentz and Poincaré. A wealthy citizen of Darmstadt had bequeathed a large sum of money to be given as a prize to the first mathematician to solve the seventeenth-century problem known as "Fermat's Last Theorem"; until a recipient was found, the interest on the legacy was used to finance the lectures that attracted to Göttingen students and teachers from all over the world. Hilbert once expressed the hope that no one would ever solve the problem and so deprive Göttingen of the prestige of these lectures.

Even though Simon was to spend too short a time at Göttingen, the impression made on him by what could be achieved by the co-operation of science and industry and by the frequent gatherings of scientists from different universities and countries remained with him to influence many of his most strongly held beliefs. As at Munich he had been fortunate enough to study under one of the greatest scientists of his age, Sommer-feld, so at Göttingen he encountered in Courant and Tamman teachers of a similar reputation. As might be expected the greater part of his course was devoted to mathematics, though he managed to include some classes in philosophy, chemistry and experimental electricity within the framework of his main subjects, analytical geometry and algebra. Reports were given only at the end of a course; Simon received none from Göttingen since the war prevented him from returning, as he had intended, after completing his military service for which the university gave him leave of absence.

That Simon had made the most of his brief courses at Munich and Göttingen was shown by the speed with which he was able to complete his doctor's degree after the war. He had extended and co-ordinated his mathematical studies, had enlarged his knowledge of the various branches of physics, and had proved himself an exceptionally good experimentalist. His interest had been sufficiently aroused for him to retain the facts that he had acquired, and his success had laid the bogey of his school failures. Until he began to take an interest in science, he had been so bored that he had learned as little as possible. Once his attention was caught and he realized that the view from the mountain top was worth the drudgery of the climb, he had to discipline himself severely to assimilate the details that provided the essential footholds. His early university experience taught him what he should have learned at school – how to work. Years later he wrote to his wife, worried about one of their daughters who showed no desire to concen-trate on the learning of tedious subjects: "She is very much like me as a child in this respect – and by the way now also to a certain extent – and I had no help whatsoever from my educa-tion. It needed very great effort to overcome this later on."

What his family remembered about the period at Munich and Göttingen was the good time Franz had. Gradually the quiet, unsociable, scholastically unsuccessful boy emerged into the mature man, with his irrepressible curiosity, piquant wit, happy self-confidence and social ease. He possessed the ability, so often lacking in the young, of sizing people up, and, though in fact acutely sensitive, of concealing his feelings. In many ways he was a typical Berliner — witty, shrewd, quick in repartee — and these qualities, latent in him as a schoolboy, flowered away from home, in the appreciative company of his contemporaries. The photographs of the period show that he was physically attractive; the keen eyes behind the glasses, the firm mouth adorned in those days with the perpetual cigarette, the slim, delicate hands, the taut figure, are all very much father to the man. As a man and as a student he gained from this brief period of independence a maturity capable of withstanding the effects of the physical and mental holocaust into which he was plunged.

Military service for German civilians was for a period of two years, though for those who were following a course of higher education this was reduced to one. Simon spent his year attached to the artillery at Augsburg, a sleepy market town with a growing engineering industry, some paper mills and textile factories. Its main claim to fame was the autumn fair — "Herbstplaerrer" — which Bertolt Brecht remembered in "Die Durchsicht meiner ersten Stucke", but for Simon it possessed only one virtue — the train to Munich. Nothing broke the monotony of endless drill and grooming of horses, while discipline and petty tyranny were administered by bullying non-commissioned officers and evaded by bribing them. These representatives of Germany's incorruptible army made it their business to know where the money lay and exerted upon the militiamen in their charge an insidious sort of blackmail. "My wife is keen on having a piano," and, since the men knew that until she had one their lives would not be worth living, they clubbed together to buy her one. As an alternative to cleaning latrines a pair of opera glasses for the N.C.O. was suggested to the rich man's son. Added to these unsalubrious practices was the overt anti-Semitism which led Simon later, after war broke out, to ask to be transferred to another regiment.

His parents kept the letter he wrote them on the eve of war:

Augsburg, 31.7.14

Dear Parents,

At last I get around to writing to you. The day before yesterday we had another artillery practice. When we got back in the morning everything was still quite quiet. You couldn't find out anything